Kacper

Na temat czytania bajki „Jaś i pnącze fasoli":

„Jaś i pnącze fasoli" jest znaną i często czytaną bajką napisaną dla dzieci, które dopiero zaczynają czytać. Wszystkie książeczki z poziomu 1, z serii dla dzieci rozpoczynających czytanie, mają proste teksty zawierające około 200 słów łatwych do przeczytania. Słowa te są powszechnie używane w materiałach do nauki czytania i ćwiczenia wymowy. Zdania w bajkach z tego poziomu są krótkie. Ilustracje zamieszczone przy tekście są dla dzieci dodatkową rozrywką i powinny być z nimi omawiane w celu pełnego zrozumienia puenty. Książka ta sprawi Państwu i dzieciom wiele przyjemności przy wspólnym czytaniu. Pomoże ona dziecku rozwijać umiejętność czytania. Ogólnie zaleca się ją dzieciom w wieku od 5 do 6 roku życia.

Moja pierwsza czytanka

poziom:

1

Jaś i pnącze fasoli

Dawno, dawno temu w małej, wiejskiej chatce mieszkał z rodzicami chłopiec o imieniu Jasio. Wszyscy ciężko pracowali, ale byli bardzo szczęśliwi. Nie mieli żadnych zmartwień, ponieważ posiadali trzy magiczne przedmioty: worek złotych monet, który zawsze był pełen, kurkę znoszącą złote jajka i czarodziejską harfę, która sama pięknie grała.

Jednak pewnego dnia,
we wsi pojawił się
przerażający olbrzym.

Jaś i jego matka byli teraz bardzo biedni.
Pewnego dnia, kiedy Jasio razem
z wiewiórką zbierali gałęzie, matka
stwierdziła ze smutkiem:
– Jasiu, musisz pójść na targ i sprzedać
krowę! Nie mamy już co jeść!
Jasio z wiewiórką
o imieniu Okruszek
zabrali krowę
i wyruszyli w drogę.

W lesie spotkali starego,
obdartego człowieka,
podpierającego się laską.
– Kupię od ciebie krowę
– powiedział – w zamian,
dam ci te trzy zaczarowane fasolki.

– Matko! Sprzedałem krowę
za te trzy zaczarowane fasolki!
Ale matka zamiast się ucieszyć,
uniosła się gniewem.
Wieczorem, Jasio poszedł spać smutny
i głodny. Ale ranek przyniósł
niespodziankę. Obudził go ptak, który
sfrunął przez okno wołając: – Patrz Jasiu!
Przez noc fasolki urosły i zmieniły się
w ogromne fasolowe drzewa.

Pnącza fasoli były tak wysokie,
że sięgały chmur.
Okruszek zaraz na nie wskoczył,
a za nim wspinał się po fasoli żądny
przygód Jasio.
Dotarli do ogromnego zamku.
Zdumiony Jaś spostrzegł stojącą
w drzwiach żonę olbrzyma.

Żona olbrzyma była miła
i dała Jasiowi coś do jedzenia.
Gdy już się najadł,
zaczął się przyglądać przerażająco
wielkim komnatom i meblom.
Nagle usłyszeli, że Olbrzym zbliża się
do zamku! Jego grzmiące kroki sprawiały,
że cały zamek trząsł się w posadach.
W ostatniej chwili
Jasio wskoczył pod stół.

Gdy Olbrzym zasiadł do stołu,
Jaś zobaczył na stole
rodzinne skarby:
kurkę, harfę i worek złota.

Gdy Olbrzym wyszedł,
Jaś złapał kurkę,
wyskoczył przez okno
i po liściach fasoli zsunął
się na ziemię.

Jaś opowiedział matce,
że tam wysoko
mieszka Olbrzym,
który ukradł im worek
monet, złotą kurkę
i harfę.

Jaś powiedział matce,
że musi wrócić do zamku
Olbrzyma,
by odebrać pozostałe skarby.

Gdy wyskakiwał,
z harfą pod pachą,
harfa zagrała, co zbudziło
Olbrzyma! Olbrzym ruszył
w pogoń za Jasiem.

Ale Jaś był szybszy.
Kiedy dotarł na ziemię,
złapał siekierę i zaczął
rąbać pnącze fasoli.
Ciął z całej siły.
Olbrzym zapadł się pod
ziemię.

Matka Jasia uściskała syna mocno.
– Jesteś dzielnym i mądrym
chłopcem! – zawołała – Jakże się
teraz cieszę, że sprzedałeś krowę
za te trzy czarodziejskie fasolki!

Livingdying

poems of

Cid

Corman

A New Directions Book

PS
3553
.O65
L5

Manufactured in the United States of America
Published simultaneously in Canada by McClelland & Stewart, Limited

Designed by Roderick Stinehour and printed at The Stinehour Press, Lunenburg, Vermont

New Directions Books are published for James Laughlin
by New Directions Publishing Corporation,
333 Sixth Avenue, New York 10014

Leben ist Tod,
und Tod ist auch ein Leben.

for Ted

More song. What
more mountain

than the one
that is: wished.

I

STRANGER, tell the Lacedemonians
we remain here, obedient to their laws.

YOUNG strong and willing
Sword in hand alone
How much ground covered
Chang-I to Yu-Chou
Drank at the Yi's source
Got to no man's land
Nothing but old graves
Of them two high points
Chuang-Chou Po-Ya rest
No longer around
I have gone far—why

WE drink
to each
other
mountain
flowers

One cup
leads to
others
others

Mind floats
body
lies by

Go friend
Tomorrow

Morning

And don't
forget

Your lute

TEN years living dying alone
Why remember
How forget
Miles and miles away
Cold thought thinking
If we met would you know me
Face dust
Hair frost

Dreaming last night found me home
At your window
You primping
Turning to see me
Tears for your eyes
Year after year what eats the heart
Moon grave
Squat pine

MOURNING—
most
what is
  was

The loss
weighs and
holds at
  O

No one
to hear
(windless)
  trees

Leaves
left—is
that what
  stays

Words—
this breath—
you—no—
  I?

So gentle
her ways
no words are
for eyes

Quietly
arrayed
she exceeds
our hours

Who sees
feels himself
yielding

the body
brimming
light lifting.

THE UNFORGIVABLE

CHEAT friends mock art
Spit at the saint
OK—but dont
Interrupt heart.

ONLY you, to whom
creation is due and does
return, O death, are
eternal, through you
do we let go and
rest—not happy, no, but free
from ancient ache. To think
of a dark night
on a dark night con-
fuses; the heart finds
nothing to cling to:
released from fear
it merely rises to
motions of slow time.
We were: and the ghosts
and nightmares
of infancy stray
like lost remembrances:
memory advances
as life does: but what is
memory to terror! What were we?
What was the point
to what we called life?
Today life seems to us
mystery, miracle, even as death—
all a-shroud—
seems to the living. And just
as we lived fleeing
death, so now do we flee
the leaping flame
we quenched—
not happy, ever, but free—
for blessedness is as much
denied the dying as the dead.

THAT there
                sky
the tree
            shake
light
        yawn
bird
        song

What you do
                to be
here

What you done
                    years
man

His eyes from seeing only bars
are so tired they no longer see.
As if this were a world of bars
and beyond this world no other.

The pad of the easiest stride
revolves in the smallest circuit—
force dancing around the center
of an immense paralyzed will.

Sometimes, however, the pupil
opens wide : An image enters
and pierces the long restrained limbs
and stops being within the heart.

II

THE CHILD

ALL gone out
alone too
dark to sleep

drifting eyes
clinging wall
ceiling light

window of
someone's car
hurrying

by. Mama!
Here is your
house, your child.

MAKING LOVE

Am I the
only child
who has grown
old in vain?

The others,
it seems, have
all somehow
managed things,

learned to walk
and talk and
feel at home
wherever

they happened
to be. And
I have not—
have no knack

for any
thing but ob-
stinacy—
for hanging

on—finding
myself the
genius of
a body

whose meaning
still escapes
me. Even
I who say

"I"—small spark
of breath called
soul by some—
doubt *that* and

am surprised,
of course, when
this woman,
my wife, turns

to me—me
no less—at
night—to be
reassured!

And I—half-
smiling—like
a fool—and
half-crying

—like one lost—
know that we
are what we
were—infants—

as death—our
death—reveals
us more and
more at birth.

THE BAPTISM

DIPPED into
cold night
sea

to draw this
gasping
out

glad to be
back on
shore

shivering
naked
flame.

THE WORLD
AT SANTO SPIRITO

Oɴ the roof
gods gazing
over
olives

almost feel
poppies
burst, see
nothing is

but trembles
divine, more
more sea
down there

where the
garden halts
and the sands
smooth out.

Only
the sun
to mull things
make splendor

wonder air
sky spread
beyond gulls
wings gulls

cry. O
citadel!
protecting
what? All

horizons
vanish
in the dark,
descend

and know
empty niche,
naked
shadow, flesh

breath grow
small, snail bless
lintel,
lizard wall.

THE DREAM

Beyond this room
another, the
bewildering
array a world

presents. And now
to live here. Pro–
prietary.
As if I had

the time to go
on leisurely
exploring one
room and the next.

As if one door
does not open
blank. My shadow,
in relief, there.

THE FEAT

DEAD, who can say,
I have been? One

may imagine,
but body knows.

Nothing can go
that far and not

have gone too far—
or has it? One

may visit. He
did, who looked back

beyond song to
the impulse of

singing. Ascend
from the heart, heart.

THE ANSWER

How sleep anyhow? if
that were it. World's
too bang; even in dreams
precipitate. Death's

no health-cure: a resort
to which one turns
in the last instance. No.
It's always present,

like vanity, like flesh.
Don't make me laugh
or I'll cry; that's the cry.
Hear me, my silence,

in silence. The morning
answers nothing,
yet I have asked for light.
Light like light is light.

THE
POET

In that
cold he is
known by

like his
friend the wind
sweeping

shadows
along a
summit

laughing
at himself
laughing.

THE JOURNAL

I shall go out
again and find
a tree, trees, pines,
mountains of pine

If my silence
succeeds in song,
you will hear of
it from the winds.

III

THE
SUPERFLUITIES

RAGS hanging
out of his
overalls'
backpockets

to shine knobs
on churchdoors,
which is what
he now does—

as if to
confirm a
guess, to say:
dark as I

am, the sun
on a clear
day only
acknowled-

ges what is
done is here,
as I am,
doing more.

MISTER
YOUNG

Not grace, Lord knows, but
a fury.
To bury meat
rather than

give it to people,
those at least
who were given
to mocking

him. Dignity is
like that. Mean
and silly, but
anyhow

marvellous. There is
in most men
equal malice,
ignorance

and innocence. He,
for instance,
cares enough for
his mink and

chinchilla out in
Idyho

to inter their
pelts for no

other reason than
sentiment.
Poor critter, man,
who often

does worst by his own
brethren. He,
who caught bare in
a fire with

only a shirt on,
said that he'd
just as soon toss
that back in.

"Five miles either way
from the two
nearest towns" is
near enough.

THE
COUNTER

talking, the
two of us only,
over soup

Mischa, it's
his place, raises
the question of

water, how
this guy comes in
for coffee in-

sists on a
glass of water, 3
glasses full

as if he hadn't   "in this" he nods
enough, alone,   "I know
to do   I am right." I say

borrows a   nothing. It's good
toothpick and—   to be wrong too
and asks for the key   sometimes. But

to the john, that's   never argue with
an awful lot   one who
for a dime   has to be right.

THE INVITATION

To be taken
by the beret
for a fairy
very USA—

but up against
the staggering
black man, and me
licking away at

an ice-cream cone,
to answer and
yet not offend
places my free hand

on his warm cheek
saying, I'd go
with you, my friend,
but I'm going to

another now.
That abashes.
He sees me feel
his face grow warmer.

THE GENTLE MAN

IT's not that
he hasn't
a lovely
wife and a

lovely pair
of daughters
and a nice
house in a

nice part of
a nice town—
but that he
hasn't yet

made any
sense of it
for himself
and so he

goes away
quietly
to die in
his own way.

AUNT ROSE

Condolences for
one who painted her
flesh against the years.

Against the years what
words? Death's countenance
brooks no epithet.

PARC

In the park
on a slab.
Children
prancing.

Who can
awaken
her? Night
the gate and

the river
outside.
Island
again and

stars. O-
pening far
a cry
a silence.

THE BLESSING

AT the temple
on the hill
a slat from an
old crate requiring

visitors to
dress properly
(not in underwear)
for this place

not to make noise
nor swipe the moss nor
litter the ground
nor loiter

We go—passing
plaques of Buddha
blessing us
for doing nothing.

THE CONDIMENT

GRASS
comes over
the slope
or nearly

across
the grass
the salt of
shadows

pigeons
into the
emptying
air.

IV

THE DANCE

FINALLY
one by one
she lets go
the veils and

you see—de-
lirious-
ly—there is
nothing left.

Look now in
to the great
emptiness

What comes as
her gift comes
in a plate.

THE LOCK

To open or close,
stay in or stay out—
the key perfectly

fits in the lock turns,
weighs in the pocket.
But the skeleton

suits every door,
the master breaker,
reminding each of

us who the host is
here and who the guest
and who the poor thief.

THE JOB

How to put things
together
as if they were
not broken

how the hands
in dialogues of
plaster and clay
restored

feel ruins fit
finding that
everything
turns out to be

something
inseparable
from what was
otherwise thought.

As if it had thrown itself away
in the middle of the road the dog—
not dead—exhausted—barking all night

ready to be silent—if possible—
until night returns. But now—rising—
reluctantly—as I pass—not sure

what I may be up to—standing there—
with a weary abject look of fear—
not even claiming to be a dog.

IT's always too late
to learn. The ball we
threw against his wall

allowing the sick
neighbor no sleep drew
anger we thought was

selfish, as it was,
as we were too. Now,
ill, I hear a child

banging an empty
moment at my wall
and try to lie still.

On the blank
paper a
speck, in it

almost, it
seems, but to
my eyes—not

always re-
liable—
it moves at

an immense
distance at
great speed and

yet has not
moved at all—
for the white

space clings to
it as to
a meaning.

I bring you
a bag of
oranges—

the sweetest
oranges—
and you take

them out one
by one and
set them on

a white plate—
spheres of a
pyramid.

MOTHER, you will die.
In a few years, more
or less. I have the

doctor's word for it.
What is there to say
or see or do? Day

extends day. Body
bends to earth to drink
a dish of shadow.